Spanish

Hola.

Written By:
Kim Mitzo Thompson
Karen Mitzo Hilderbrand

Illustrated By:
Steve Ruttner
Mark Paskiet
Betsy Snyder

Cover Illustration By:
Sandy Haight

Musical Arrangement and Vocal Coach:
Hal Wright

Language Experts:

Language Vocal Coach:
Lea Jane Berinati

Music Professor:
Lalo Davila
MTSU

Various Translators:
Corporate Language Services

Spanish Teachers:
Martha Pero and Heather Spencer

Note: Not all authorities and textbooks agree on which letters make up the Spanish alphabet. According to the Real Academia Española, which is considered the arbiter of what's official Spanish, the following letters and digraphs make up the Spanish alphabet: a, b, c, ch, d, e, f, g, h, i, j, k, l, ll, m, n, ñ, o, p, q, r, s, t, u, v, w, x, y, z

While the Academia no longer considers rr a separate letter in the Spanish alphabet, the rr is included in "The Alphabet Song" on this music CD; the rr or "erreh" is a significant phoneme in the Spanish language, essential to correct pronunciation and usage by those learning to speak the language.

Twin Sisters Productions, LLC • (800) 248-TWIN • www.twinsisters.com

Table of Contents

Spanish Lyrics

Activities

Spanish

The Alphabet Song

The alphabet is easy to learn.
Speak in rhythm. Each letter gets a turn.
The alphabet is easy to learn.
Speak in rhythm. Each letter gets a turn.
(Repeat)

Can you say the alphabet in Spanish?
It's easy if you say the alphabet in rhythm.
Listen to me.

A, B, C, CH, D, E, F, G, H, I, J, K, L,
LL, M, N, Ñ, O, P, Q, R, RR, S, T, U,
V, W, X, Y, Z
(Chorus)

It's your turn now. Repeat after me:

A, B, C, CH, D, E, F   A, B, C, CH, D, E, F
G, H, I, J, K, L   G, H, I, J, K, L
LL, M, N, Ñ, O, P   LL, M, N, Ñ, O, P
Q, R, RR, S, T, U, V   Q, R, RR, S, T, U, V
W, X, Y, Z   W, X, Y, Z
(Chorus)

One more time.

A, B, C, CH, D, E, F   A, B, C, CH, D, E, F
G, H, I, J, K, L   G, H, I, J, K, L
LL, M, N, Ñ, O, P   LL, M, N, Ñ, O, P
Q, R, RR, S, T, U, V   Q, R, RR, S, T, U, V
W, X, Y, Z   W, X, Y, Z
(Chorus 2x)

Spanish

Counting From One To Ten

I'm going to teach you how to count from one to ten,
and when we're through we will sing a counting song.

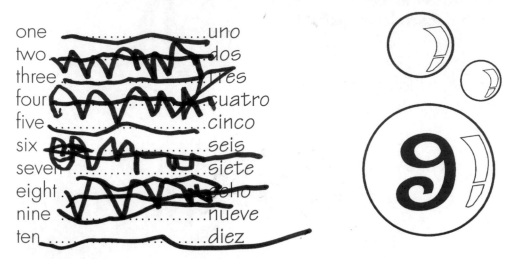

one ....uno
two....................dos
three..................tres
four...................cuatro
five...................cinco
six ....seis
seven.................siete
eight ....ocho
nine ....nueve
ten ....diez

Good! Now, let's say the numbers one more time.

one ....uno
two........................dos
three.....................tres
four.......................cuatro
five.......................cinco
six ....seis
seven ....siete
eight......................ocho
nine ....nueve
ten ....diez

Oh, I can count from one to ten, one to ten, one to ten.
I can count from one to ten, listen to me.
Uno, dos, tres, cuatro, cinco, seis, siete, ocho, nueve, y diez.
I can count from one to ten, listen to me.
(Repeat)

Spanish

Numbers To Twenty

Jumping rope to a counting song—
count with me and jump along.
Let's count to the number ten,
then up to twenty, and we'll start again.

one ....uno
two.............................dos
three ....tres
four ....cuatro
five ....cinco
six ....seis
seven ....siete
eight ....ocho
nine ....nueve
ten ....diez

Jumping rope to a counting song—
count with me and jump along.
Up to the number twenty we'll go,
and all the numbers soon you'll know.

eleven ....once
twelve ....doce
thirteen ....trece
fourteen ....catorce
fifteen ....quince
sixteen ....dieciséis
seventeen ....diecisiete
eighteen ....dieciocho
nineteen ....diecinueve
twenty ....veinte

Jumping rope to a counting song—
I'm tired of counting and jumping along.
We know our numbers, each and every one.
Counting to twenty was lots of fun.

Spanish

Learning Colors

We are going to teach you to
pronounce each color name,
and then we will sing a color song.
Are you ready?

red.............................rojo
blue............................azul
green..........................verde
yellow.........................amarillo
orange.......................anaranjado
purple........................morado
pink...........................rosado
brown.........................café
black ....negro
white..........................blanco

Great. Now let's say each color in
Spanish, and then in English.

rojo............................red
azul............................blue
verde.........................green
amarillo......................yellow
anaranjado..................orange
morado.......................purple
rosado........................pink
café...........................brown
negro..........................black
blanco.........................white

Red is *rojo*. Red is *rojo*.
Rojo is red. *Rojo* is red.
Learning all the colors is fun,
and colors are for everyone.
I like to shout and let you know
that red is *rojo*.

Blue is *azul*. Blue is *azul*.
Azul is blue. *Azul* is blue.
Learning all the colors is fun,
and colors are for everyone.
I like to shout and let you know
that blue is *azul*.

Green is *verde*. Green is *verde*.
Verde is green. *Verde* is green.
Learning all the colors is fun,
and colors are for everyone.
I like to shout and let you know
that green is *verde*.

Yellow is *amarillo*. Yellow is *amarillo*.
Amarillo is yellow. *Amarillo* is yellow.
Learning all the colors is fun,
and colors are for everyone.
I like to shout and let you know
that yellow is *amarillo*.

Orange is *anaranjado*.
Orange is *anaranjado*.
Anaranjado is orange.
Anaranjado is orange.
Learning all the colors is fun,
and colors are for everyone.
I like to shout and let you know
that orange is *anaranjado*.

Purple is *morado*. Purple is *morado*.
Morado is purple. *Morado* is purple.
Learning all the colors is fun,
and colors are for everyone.
I like to shout and let you know
that purple is *morado*.

Pink is *rosado*. Pink is *rosado*.
Rosado is pink. *Rosado* is pink.
Learning all the colors is fun,
and colors are for everyone.
I like to shout and let you know
that pink is *rosado*.

Brown is *café*. Brown is *café*.
Café is brown. *Café* is brown.
Learning all the colors is fun,
and colors are for everyone.
I like to shout and let you know
that brown is *café*.

Black is *negro*. Black is *negro*.
Negro is black. *Negro* is black.
Learning all the colors is fun,
and colors are for everyone.
I like to shout and let you know
that black is *negro*.

White is *blanco*. White is *blanco*.
Blanco is white. *Blanco* is white.
Learning all the colors is fun,
and colors are for everyone.
I like to shout and let you know
that white is *blanco*.

Spanish

The Days Of The Week

You can learn the days of the week if you listen carefully.
domingo, lunes, martes, miércoles, jueves, viernes, sábado

Sunday ....domingo
Monday ....lunes
Tuesday ....martes
Wednesday ....miércoles, Wednesday,
Thursday ....jueves
Friday ....viernes
Saturday ....sábado

Si escuchas con cuidado,
puedes aprender los días de la semana.
Sunday, Monday, Tuesday, Wednesday, Thursday, Friday, Saturday

domingo ....Sunday
lunes ....Monday
martes ....Tuesday
miércoles ....Wednesday, miércoles
jueves ....Thursday
viernes ....Friday
sábado ....Saturday

We've just learned the days of the week.
Next time won't you sing with me?
Hemos aprendido los días de la semana.
¿No cantarás conmigo la próxima vez?

Spanish

Name The Animals

Can you name the animals?
Can you say their names?
Can you name the animals
in this animal naming game?

(Repeat)

There's an elephant, *elefante*,
a lion, *león*,
a seal, *foca*,
and a bear, *oso*.

I see a monkey, *mono*,
a giraffe, *jirafa*,
a tiger, *tigre*,
and a snake, *serpiente*.

The hippos are sleeping.
Los hipopótamos duermen.

The kangaroos are hopping.
Los canguros saltan.

The birds are singing.
Los pájaros trinan.

And the zebras don't make a sound.
Y las cebras no hacen ruido.

(Chorus)

(Repeat song)

(Chorus 2x)

In this animal naming game.

Spanish

The Hello Song

(Chorus 1:)
Hello, hello, hello to you.
I wish to say, I wish to say hello to you.
Hola, hola, hola a ti.
Quiero decir, quiero decir hola a ti.

Hello, how are you?	Hola. ¿Cómo estás?
I am good.	Estoy bien.
Hola. ¿Cómo estás?	Hello, how are you?
Estoy así así.	I am so-so.

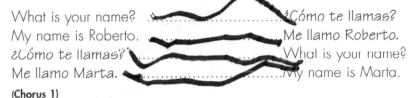

(Chorus 2:)
Hola, hola, hola a ti.
Quiero decir, quiero decir hola a ti.
Hello, hello, hello to you.
I wish to say, I wish to say hello to you.

What is your name?	¿Cómo te llamas?
My name is Roberto.	Me llamo Roberto.
¿Cómo te llamas?	What is your name?
Me llamo Marta.	My name is Marta.

(Chorus 1)

Are you in school?	¿Estás en la escuela?
Yes, I am in school.	Sí, estoy en la escuela.
¿Qué aprendes?	What are you learning?
Aprendo idiomas distintos.	I am learning different languages.

(Chorus 2)

It was nice to speak with you.	Fue agradable hablar contigo.
Goodbye Roberto, see you tomorrow.	Adiós Roberto, hasta mañana.
Fue agradable hablar contigo.	It was nice to speak with you.
Adiós Marta, hasta luego.	Goodbye Marta, see you later.

(Chorus 3:)
Goodbye, goodbye, goodbye to you.
I wish to say, I wish to say goodbye to you.
Adiós, adiós, adiós a ti.
Quiero decir, quiero decir adiós a ti.

¡Adiós!

Spanish

Let's Eat

We're sitting around waiting to eat.
Grab your fork, come on, let's eat!
Estamos sentados esperando comer.
Agarre tu tenedor, vamos, ¡A comer!

Please pass the...

chicken ....el pollo
potatoes............las papas
carrots ....las zanahorias
bread ....el pan
meat ....la carne
corn ....el maíz
rice............el arroz
salad............la ensalada
(Chorus)

Por favor pase...

el pollo............chicken
las papas............potatoes
las zanahorias ....carrots
el pan ....bread
la carne ....meat
el maíz............corn
el arroz............rice
la ensalada............salad
(Chorus)

Please pass the...

fish ....el pescado
beans ....los frijoles
apples............las manzanas
milk............la leche
peas ....los guisantes
bananas............los plátanos
pie ....el pastel
cake ....la torta
(Chorus)

Por favor pase...

el pescado ....fish
los frijoles ....beans
las manzanas............apples
la leche ....milk
los guisantes ....peas
los plátanos............bananas
el pastel ....pie
la torta ....cake
(Chorus)

My Family Is Special

My family is special. ....Mi familia es muy querida.
Let's learn how to say their names. ......Aprendamos a decir sus nombres.

We call them............................Se llaman...
mother ....madre
father ....padre
sister ....hermana
brother ....hermano
grandma ....abuela
grandpa ....abuelo
aunt ....tía
uncle ....tío

(Chorus 1:)
My family is special. ....Mi familia es muy querida.
We work and play together ....Trabajamos y jugamos juntos
and have fun. ....y nos divertimos.
My family is special. ....Mi familia es muy querida.
Laughing and learning, ...Riendo y aprendiendo,
growing together, ...creciendo juntos,
we're a team. ....somos un equipo.

We call them............................Se llaman...
mother ....madre
father ....padre
sister ....hermana
brother ....hermano
grandma ....abuela
grandpa ....abuelo
aunt ....tía
uncle ....tío

(Chorus 1)
(Repeat names with Spanish words first.)

(Chorus 2:)
Mi familia es muy querida. ....My family is special.
Trabajamos y jugamos juntos ......We work and play together
y nos divertimos. ....and have fun.
Mi familia es muy querida. ....My family is special.
Riendo y aprendiendo, ...Laughing and learning,
creciendo juntos, ...growing together,
somos un equipo. ....we're a team.

Spanish

The Ocean Blue

The ocean is filled with many interesting things.
El *océano está lleno de muchas cosas interesantes.*
You might find:

fish, *peces* whales, *ballenas* crabs, *cangrejos* sharks, *tiburones*
dolphins, *delfines* shells, *conchas* seals, *focas*

In the ocean blue there are lots of fish swimming all around.
Fish, fish, *peces, peces,* fish, fish, *peces, peces,*
fish, fish, *peces, peces* swimming all around.

In the ocean blue there are great big whales splashing all around.
Whales, whales, *ballenas, ballenas,* whales, whales, *ballenas, ballenas,*
whales, whales, *ballenas, ballenas* splashing all around.

In the ocean blue there are tiny crabs hiding under rocks.
Crabs, crabs, *cangrejos, cangrejos,* crabs, crabs, *cangrejos, cangrejos,*
crabs, crabs, *cangrejos, cangrejos* hiding under rocks.

In the ocean blue there are big mean sharks chasing other fish.
Sharks, sharks, *tiburones, tiburones,* sharks, sharks, *tiburones, tiburones,*
sharks, sharks, *tiburones, tiburones* chasing other fish.

In the ocean blue there are dolphins that are jumping in the air.
Dolphins, dolphins, *delfines, delfines,* dolphins, dolphins, *delfines, delfines,*
dolphins, dolphins, *delfines, delfines* jumping in the air.

In the ocean blue there are pretty shells ready to be found.
Shells, shells, *conchas, conchas,* shells, shells, *conchas, conchas,*
shells, shells, *conchas, conchas* ready to be found.

In the ocean blue there are friendly seals sliding on the ice.
Seals, seals, *focas, focas,* seals, seals, *focas, focas,*
seals, seals, *focas, focas* sliding on the ice.

The ocean blue is lots of fun. Let's swim and ride the waves.
Swim, swim, *nadar, nadar,* swim, swim, *nadar, nadar,*
swim, swim, *nadar, nadar.* Swim and ride the waves.

fish, *peces* whales, *ballenas* crabs, *cangrejos* sharks, *tiburones*
dolphins, *delfines* shells, *conchas* seals, *focas*

Swimming all around.

Spanish

Five Day Weather Forecast

What is the weather like today? ......¿Qué tiempo hace hoy?
It is sunny. ....Hace sol.

What is the weather like today? ......¿Qué tiempo hace hoy?
It is cloudy. ....Está nublado.

What is the weather like today? ......¿Qué tiempo hace hoy?
It is raining. ....Está lloviendo.

What is the weather like today? ......¿Qué tiempo hace hoy?
It is snowing. ....Está nevando.

What is the weather like today? ......¿Qué tiempo hace hoy?
It is cold. ....Hace frío.

What is the weather like today? ......¿Qué tiempo hace hoy?
It is hot. ....Hace calor.

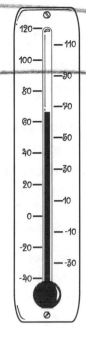

It is sunny out today, out today, out today.
It is sunny out today, *sol* means sunny.

It is cloudy out today, out today, out today.
It is cloudy out today, *nublado* means cloudy.

It is raining out today, out today, out today.
It is raining out today, *lloviendo* means raining.

It is snowing out today, out today, out today.
It is snowing out today, *nevando* means snowing.

It is cold outside today, outside today, outside today.
It is cold outside today, *frío* means cold.

It is hot outside today, outside today, outside today.
It is hot outside today, *calor* means hot.

What is the weather like today, like today, like today?
What is the weather like today? I want to play.

Is it sunny? ....¿Hace sol?
cloudy? ....¿nublado?
raining? ....¿lloviendo?
snowing? ....¿nevando?
cold? ....¿frío?
hot? ....¿calor?

What is it like today?
¿Qué tiempo hace hoy?

It is sunny out today, out today, out today.
It is sunny out today. Let's go play!

Spanish

We Are One World - Theme Song

We are one world though we come from different lands.
Language doesn't matter, nor the color of our hands.
Together we can learn to live in peace and harmony.
Learning, helping, growing together in this land of unity.

We are one world. We are one voice,
crying out to every nation that peace is our first choice.
Our faces are different colors, and the language that we speak.
But our hearts and minds are united, and each country so unique.

We are one world.

(Repeat song)
(Chorus 2x)
We are one world.
We are one world.

Spanish

Numbers One To Five

Match the number to the correct picture. Use the spaces to practice writing each number in Spanish.

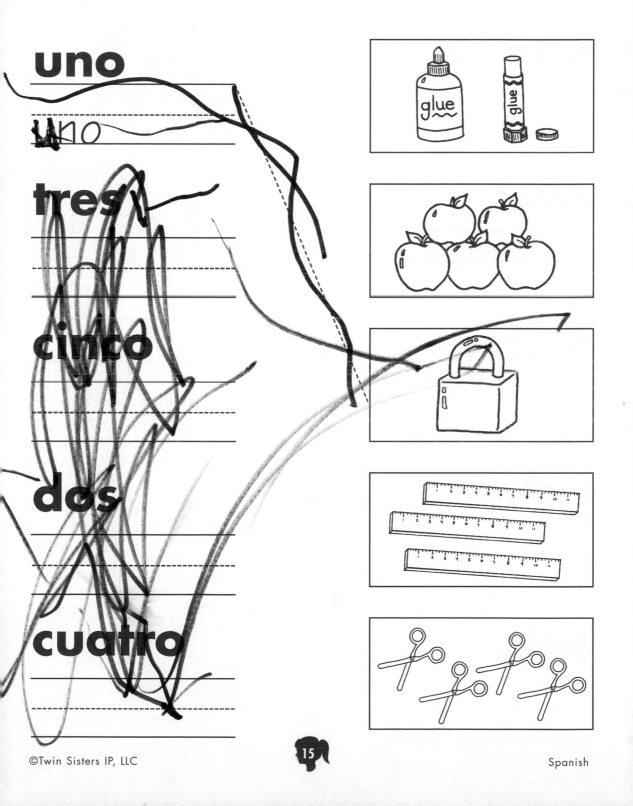

uno

uno

tres

cinco

dos

cuatro

Spanish

Numbers Six To Ten

Match the number to the correct picture. Use the spaces to practice writing each number in Spanish.

nueve

diez

siete

ocho

seis

Spanish

Learning Our Colors

Color the picture by the numbers.

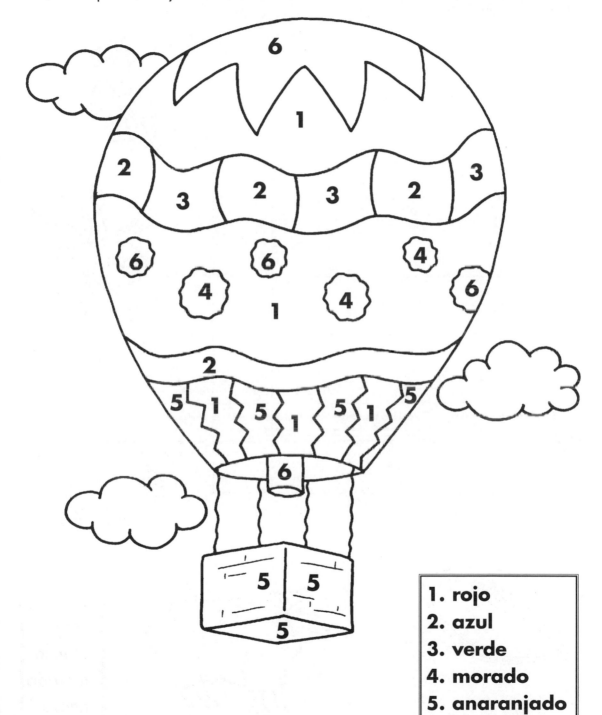

1. rojo
2. azul
3. verde
4. morado
5. anaranjado
6. amarillo

Spanish

Color Crossword Puzzle

Write the Spanish color word that best describes each picture in the crossword puzzle.

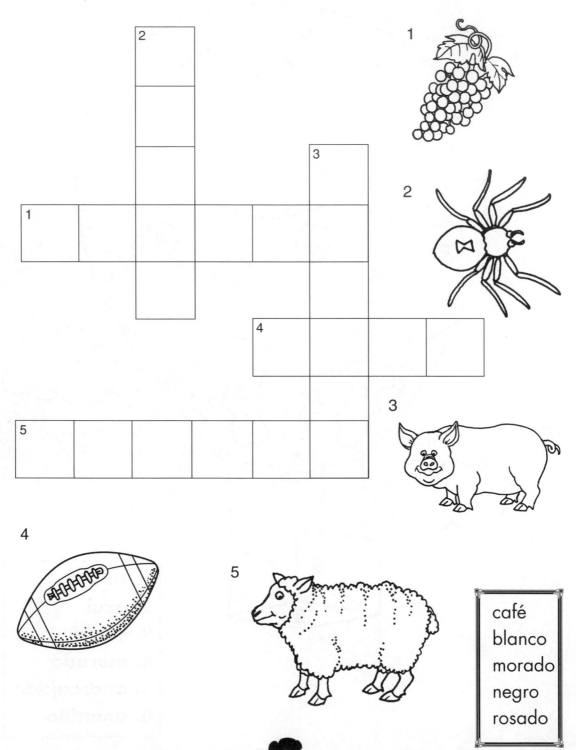

café
blanco
morado
negro
rosado

Spanish

Family Names

Practice writing each name in Spanish.

mother

father

sister

brother

grandma

grandpa

Spanish

Learning Our Weather Words

It's sunny.	Hace sol.
It's cloudy.	Está nublado.
It's raining.	Está lloviendo.
It's snowing.	Está nevando.
It's cold.	Hace frío.
It's hot.	Hace calor.

Look at the pictures and write the correct Spanish phrase in the blank.

Spanish

What Is The Weather Like Today?

Draw a picture showing what the weather is like according to the description.

¿Qué tiempo hace hoy?
Hace sol.

¿Qué tiempo hace hoy?
Está lloviendo.

¿Qué tiempo hace hoy?
Está nublado.

¿Qué tiempo hace hoy?
Está nevando.

Spanish

Learn 100 Words in Spanish

Aprende 100 palabras en inglés

colors/los colores

red	rojo	purple	morado
blue	azul	pink	rosado
green	verde	brown	café
yellow	amarillo	black	negro
orange	anaranjado	white	blanco

days of the week/los días de la semana

Sunday	domingo	Thursday	jueves
Monday	lunes	Friday	viernes
Tuesday	martes	Saturday	sábado
Wednesday	miércoles		

numbers/los números

one	uno	eleven	once
two	dos	twelve	doce
three	tres	thirteen	trece
four	cuatro	fourteen	catorce
five	cinco	fifteen	quince
six	seis	sixteen	dieciséis
seven	siete	seventeen	diecisiete
eight	ocho	eighteen	dieciocho
nine	nueve	nineteen	diecinueve
ten	diez	twenty	veinte

my family/mi familia

Mother	la madre	Grandma	la abuela
Father	el padre	Grandpa	el abuelo
Sister	la hermana	Aunt	la tía
Brother	el hermano	Uncle	el tío

weather/el tiempo

It's sunny.	Hace sol.
It's snowing.	Está nevando.
It's cloudy.	Está nublado.
It's hot.	Hace calor.
It's raining.	Está lloviendo.
It's cold.	Hace frío.

Spanish

Learn 100 Words in Spanish

Aprende 100 palabras en inglés

food/la comida

chicken	el pollo	bread	el pan
potatoes	las papas	meat	la carne
corn	el maíz	rice	el arroz
salad	la ensalada	milk	la leche
fish	el pescado	pie	el pastel
beans	los frijoles	cake	la torta
apples	las manzanas	peas	los guisantes
carrots	las zanahorias	bananas	los plátanos

animals/los animales

elephant	el elefante	snake	la serpiente
lion	el león	kangaroo	el canguro
seal	la foca	bird	el pájaro
bear	el oso	zebra	la cebra
monkey	el mono	giraffe	la jirafa
hippo	el hipopótamo	tiger	el tigre

learn more/hay más

alphabet	el alfabeto	languages	los idiomas
numbers	los números	team	el equipo
colors	los colores	hello	hola
animals	los animales	goodbye	adiós
food	la comida	yes	sí
fork	el tenedor	no	no
family	la familia	tomorrow	mañana
school	la escuela	to have fun	divertirse
to speak	hablar	to work	trabajar
to play	jugar	to laugh	reírse
to eat	comer	to learn	aprender

23

Spanish

Answer Key

Page 15

uno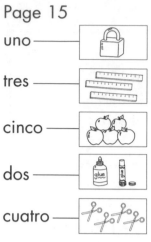

tres

cinco

dos

cuatro

Page 16

nueve

diez

siete

ocho

seis

Page 17

1. red
2. blue
3. green
4. purple
5. orange
6. yellow

Page 18

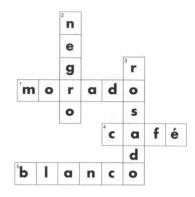

```
        ²n
         e
         g       ³r
    ¹m o r a d o  o
         o        s
              ⁴c a f é
                  d
    ⁵b l a n c o
```

 1

 2

 3

 4

 5

Page 19

madre (mother)
padre (father)
hermana (sister)
hermano (brother)
abuela (grandma)
abuelo (grandpa)

Page 20

Está nevando.   Está nublado.

Hace frío.   Hace sol.

Hace calor.   Está lloviendo.

Spanish